Exclusively U.S. CAPITOL TRIVIA

by Anthony S. Pitch

Mino Publications
Potomac, MD

Published by

Mino Publications
9009 Paddock Lane
Potomac, MD 20854

ISBN 0-931719-11-9

Printed in the United States of America

For Kayla

Also by Anthony S. Pitch

The Burning of Washington:
The British Invasion of 1814
(History Book Club selection)

Chained Eagle
(Military Book Club main selection)

The Resilient City:
How Modern Cities Recover From Disaster
(Contributing author)

A Walk in the Past—Georgetown

Congressional Chronicles

Exclusively White House Trivia

Exclusively Presidential Trivia

Exclusively First Ladies Trivia

Exclusively Washington Trivia

Washington, D.C. Sightseers' Guide

Bazak Guide to Italy

Bazak Guide to Israel

Peace

Inside Zambia—And Out

Exclusively U.S. Capitol Trivia is available at special discounts for bulk purchases for sales promotions, conventions, fundraisers or premiums.

For details, write to
Mino Publications
9009 Paddock Lane
Potomac, MD 20854

QUESTIONS

1. Who laid the southeast cornerstone on 18 September 1793?

2. When did British troops burn the Capitol?

3. Who designed the statue of *Freedom* atop the dome?

4. How many Union troops camped in the Capitol at the start of the Civil War?

5. Name the civil rights heroine who lay in honor in the Rotunda before burial.

6. Why is Daniel Webster's desk always reserved for the senior Senator from New Hampshire?

7. When did the first female minister offer the daily prayer in the House?

8. How many Senate votes are required to ratify treaties?

9. Who is second in line to the presidency?

10. When is a bright light lit above the dome?

11. Who looked at the hilly site and declared it "a pedestal waiting for a monument."?

ANSWERS

1. George Washington.
2. Wednesday 24 August 1814.
3. Thomas Crawford.
4. About 4,000.
5. Rosa Parks.
6. He represented Massachusetts but he was born and educated in New Hampshire.
7. Rev. Annalee Stewart, Methodist, in 1948.
8. Two thirds.
9. The Speaker of the House of Representatives.
10. When the House or Senate is in session.
11. Pierre L'Enfant, city planner in the 1790s.

12. What was the daily summer wage for Capitol stonecutters in the 1790s?

13. Where is the artist's mistake in the painting of *The Baptism of Pocahontas* in the Rotunda?

14. Which 1959 novel about a Senate confirmation hearing won a Pulitzer Prize and became a movie?

15. This former slave became the first African-American to serve a full term in the Senate.

16. What is the franking privilege?

17. If the Senate bells ring five times quickly what does it mean?

18. When the Supreme Court moved out of the Capitol what became of its chamber?

19. Which 19th century vice president died in the Capitol?

20. When was the first Asian-American elected to Congress?

21. How old was Sam Houston's son Andrew when appointed to the Senate to fill a vacancy from Texas?

ANSWERS

12. $1.33.

13. There are six toes on the foot of a Native American squatting on the ground.

14. *Advise and Consent* by Allen Drury.

15. Blanche Bruce (R-Miss.) 1875–81.

16. Members of Congress sign their envelopes instead of using stamps.

17. Senators have only 7 1/2 minutes left to vote.

18. It became a law library.

19. Henry Wilson, 1875.

20. Dalip Singh Saund (D-Ca.) 1956.

21. 87 years old in 1941.

22. Where does the president deliver his annual State of the Union address?

23. This Native American got special permission from the Rules Committee to wear a bolo tie in the Senate.

24. When did Samuel Morse first demonstrate his invention of the telegraph from the Capitol to Baltimore?

25. How did Clara Morris become the first souvenir and snack vendor in the Capitol during the Civil War?

26. When was the first female page appointed to the Senate?

27. Which State supplied the marble for the Hall of Columns?

28. This man died riding to the Capitol to preside over the Senate.

29. Who put an end to Rep. John Randolph's habit of bringing hunting dogs onto the House floor?

30. Where was the first Library of Congress located?

ANSWERS

22. In the chamber of the House of Representatives.

23. Sen. Ben Nighthorse Campbell (R-Co.).

24. 1844.

25. She befriended the vice president and used his influence to open a stall in the recess of a corridor.

26. 1971.

27. Massachusetts.

28. Vice President Elbridge Gerry in 1814.

29. House Speaker Henry Clay.

30. Inside the Capitol.

31. Which 19th century Italian immigrant is known as the *Michelangelo of the Capitol?*

32. This flag is flown over the Capitol every Veterans Day.

33. This Christmas eve catastrophe destroyed many of the Library of Congress's books in the Capitol.

34. How many Senators represent each State?

35. Who was the first Socialist in the House of Representatives?

36. How did John Sparkman get elected to the House and Senate on the same day in 1946?

37. Who was the first president inaugurated on the east portico?

38. Which 19th century British writer denounced Congressmen for "spitting to an excess that decency forbids me to describe."?

39. Who served only a day in the Senate?

40. Why did Senators mock Vice President John Adams, calling him *His Superfluous Excellency?*

ANSWERS

31. Constantino Brumidi.

32. The War Mothers Flag, with the blue star for children who served and a gold star for those who died in World War I.

33. A fire.

34. Two.

35. Victor Berger, a Milwaukee newspaper editor, in 1911.

36. He was running for re-election to the House when a vacancy opened up in the Senate, so his name was on both ballots.

37. Andrew Jackson.

38. Frances Trollope, in her book *Domestic Manners of the Americans.*

39. The first woman in the Senate, Rebecca Felton, 87, appointed to fill a vacancy from Georgia.

40. In the earliest debates, Adams favored high-falutin titles for elected leaders.

41. What Halloween scare swept Capitol Hill in 2003?

42. Frescoes unearthed from this ancient Mediterranean city inspired Brumidi's art in the Capitol.

43. This House page became the richest man in the world.

44. How much did Congress pay for the painting, *Apotheosis of Washington,* in the canopy of the dome?

45. A table made of surplus iron from the dome stood before this 16th president at his second inaugural.

46. Are flags flown above the Capitol available for purchase?

47. When did families of Congressmen begin accompanying them to Washington?

48. How can you tell Congress is in a night session?

49. When were desks removed from the House chamber to make way for unassigned benches?

ANSWERS

41. Two staffers passed through security in the Cannon House Office Building before their toy pistol was noticed on a security screen.

42. Pompeii.

43. Microsoft founder Bill Gates.

44. $40,000.

45. Abraham Lincoln.

46. Yes, on application to Senators and Representatives.

47. With the advent of railways.

48. A light is lit above the dome.

49. 1913.

50. When did Martha Pope become the first female Senate sergeant at arms?

51. What is spooky about the Capitol room where Daniel Webster stored his wine?

52. Can Congress pass legislation contravening the Bill of Rights?

53. This Apollo 13 astronaut won election to Congress but died only days before the swearing-in.

54. How did the Senate's "candy desk" get its name?

55. How are the original 13 States symbolized in the ceremonial House Mace?

56. Where does Congress get the authority to admit new States into the Union?

57. How many children did Capitol Architect Thomas Walter father?

58. When was the statue of *Freedom* placed on top of the dome?

59. When can you view a mural showing America's first moon landing?

ANSWERS

50. 1991.

51. A heavy marble table has been seen to vibrate occasionally and even move across the floor.

52. No.

53. John L. Swigert, Jr.

54. Former Hollywood movie star, Sen. George Murphy (R-Ca.), always distributed candy from his desk after his election in 1964.

55. By the 13 ebony rods.

56. Article IV section 3 of the Constitution.

57. 13 from two marriages.

58. 1863.

59. Muralist Allyn Cox painted this in 1975 in the north hallway of the Senate's Brumidi Corridors.

60. When do Congressional pages attend school?

61. How many terms did President George H.W. Bush serve in the House?

62. How much were the first Senators paid?

63. Why was William Halsall's painting of *First Fight of Ironclads, Monitor and Merrimac,* removed from the Capitol?

64. What are House and Senate standing committees?

65. Can a vacancy in the House be filled by appointment of a new member?

66. The National Symphony Orchestra performs on the Capitol grounds on this annual holiday.

67. How heavy is the 9 ft. 10 in. statue of King Kamehameha I donated by Hawaii?

68. Where can you view the famous "pudding stone" marble?

69. Members of the House have to be at least this age.

ANSWERS

60. In the early morning.

61. Two, 1967–71.

62. $6 per day when in session.

63. It was so large that there was no alternative wall space when removed to make way for Senate elevators.

64. Permanent committees overlooking specific subjects.

65. No. The replacement must be elected.

66. Fourth of July.

67. Almost 15 tons.

68. The speckled limestone breccia fusion of ancient rocks, passing for marble, are in columns in the Old Senate Chamber and in Statuary Hall.

69. 25 years old.

70. On what occasion is a Senator selected to read George Washington's 1796 Farewell Address?

71. What linked the House and Senate wings in the earliest years?

72. Which president saw Constantino Brumidi painting his first fresco in the Capitol?

73. Do the words *In God We Trust* appear in the House and Senate chambers?

74. When was the presidential inauguration first carried live on the internet?

75. This man worked for 64 years in the Senate but could spell based only on the sound of the words.

76. All four elected Senators from these two States were females serving simultaneously in the 109th Congress.

77. Vinnie Ream died before finishing this statue of a Cherokee for Statuary Hall.

78. How long did it take to lay the colorful Minton tiles from England in the House and Senate wings?

ANSWERS

70. Washington's birthday.

71. A 100 ft.-long covered wooden walkway.

72. Franklin Pierce.

73. Yes.

74. 1997.

75. Isaac Bassett began as a page in 1831 and died when assistant doorkeeper in 1895.

76. California and Maine.

77. Sequoyah, creator of the Cherokee alphabet.

78. 1856–1860.

79. When did the tradition begin of flying the U.S. flag continuously over the east and west fronts?

80. Which biblical psalm is quoted in the Prayer Room?

81. When was the first Chinese-American elected to the Senate?

82. Does a House or Senate resolution have the force of law?

83. What was historic about the 6th Congress 2nd Session?

84. Which areas of the mainland and offshore have Delegates representing them in Congress?

85. Who appointed Benjamin Henry Latrobe Architect of the Capitol in 1803?

86. Where is the statue of female suffrage advocate Esther Hobart Morris, honored by Wyoming?

87. When was the last time the presidential inaugural was held on 4 March?

ANSWERS

79. During World War II.

80. Psalm 16:1.

81. Hiram Fong (R-Hi.) 1959.

82. No.

83. It met in 1800 for the first time in Washington.

84. The District of Columbia, Guam, American Samoa, U.S. Virgin Islands.

85. President Thomas Jefferson.

86. In the vestibule adjoining Statuary Hall.

87. 1933.

88. When was the first time the presidential inauguration was held on 20 January?

89. Where is Confederate President Jefferson Davis painted in the canopy above the Rotunda?

90. Why did all the city's bells ring on 18 September 1893?

91. When did lice infest the Senate chamber?

92. Estimate the weight of the statue of *Freedom* above the dome.

93. In 1824 Congress voted a gift of $200,000 and 24,000 acres of land to this foreigner for helping out in the Revolutionary War.

94. On what side of the House Speaker do Democrats and Republicans sit?

95. During what years did the *Congressional Globe* carry daily proceedings of Congress?

96. This president took his vice presidential desk from the Capitol to the Oval Office.

97. How much did Congress pay New York sculptor Charles Keck for the marble bust of Vice President Harry Truman?

ANSWERS

88. 1937.

89. He is the figure holding two flaming torches, being scattered by *Freedom*, a sword-wielding woman in a scene called *War.*

90. To commemorate the centennial of the laying of the Capitol's cornerstone.

91. At the outbreak of the Civil War, when unwashed troops camped inside.

92. The woman called *Freedom* weighs nearly 15 tons.

93. The Marquis de Lafayette, for military and financial assistance given during the war.

94. Democrats on the Speaker's right and Republicans on the left.

95. 1833–1873.

96. Richard Nixon.

97. $2,500 in 1947.

98. Who was the only member of Congress to vote against U.S. participation in both World Wars?

99. When did the Senate approve the treaty to buy Alaska from Russia for $7.2 million?

100. Which State had the most Representatives the first time Congress convened in Washington?

101. It is only 7" wide and 11.25" long but this coin silver inkstand on the House Speaker's desk is treasured. Why?

102. How many of the Senators' desks date back to 1819?

103. On what date did George Washington approve the site for the Capitol?

104. When was architect Charles Bulfinch's wood and copper dome removed to make way for the current one?

105. Can the single elected Delegate from Washington, D.C. vote on the floor of the House?

106. Does the Speaker of the House have to be a member of Congress?

ANSWERS

98. Jeannette Rankin (R-Mont.), a pacifist.

99. 1867.

100. Virginia, with 20.

101. It is the oldest item in the chamber.

102. 48.

103. 28 June 1791.

104. 1856.

105. No.

106. No.

107. Which First Lady set a precedent by accompanying her husband on the inaugural parade from the Capitol?

108. Which esteemed Congressman defended Africans who had seized the slave ship *Amistad?*

109. The same flag that flew over the Capitol the day Japan attacked Pearl Harbor was flown aboard this battleship when the Japanese surrendered.

110. This House sergeant at arms was previously a Congressman from Ohio.

111. Is the gilded eagle in the Old Senate Chamber an original?

112. Almost tortured to death by a mob for virulently opposing the War of 1812, this man was later elected to the House from Maryland.

113. Was President James Monroe ever a Senator?

114. Where are the Wright brothers commemorated in art for their pioneering of manned flight?

ANSWERS

107. Helen Taft, in 1909.

108. John Quincy Adams.

109. USS *Missouri*.

110. Robert Gordon (D-Oh.).

111. Yes.

112. Alexander Contee Hanson.

113. Yes, for 3 1/2 years from 1790.

114. In the Rotunda frieze.

115. Since when has the daily edition of the *Congressional Record* been available electronically?

116. Who puts the Seal of the House on subpoenas issued by that body?

117. Where are the graves of the Italian immigrant brothers, Giuseppe and Carlo Franzoni, who beautified the Capitol in its earliest years?

118. How long did the Supreme Court meet in the Capitol before getting its own building in 1935?

119. House Speaker Nicholas Longworth married this president's daughter.

120. Why was the appointment to the Senate of President Kennedy's former press secretary, Pierre Salinger (D-Ca.), challenged unsuccessfully?

121. Why did Sen. Henry Clay flourish an alleged fragment of George Washington's coffin in 1850?

122. Until when did the House regularly meet in closed sessions?

ANSWERS

115. 1985.

116. The Clerk of the House.

117. Oak Hill Cemetery, Georgetown.

118. 125 years.

119. Teddy Roosevelt's daughter, Alice.

120. He had lived less than the minimum year in California, mandated by State law, but not required by the U.S. Constitution.

121. As a warning not to destroy the Union cemented by George Washington.

122. Through the end of the War of 1812.

123. What is an engrossed bill?

124. In which wing were two Capitol police officers killed by a gunman?

125. Who carries the Mace into the House chamber for the start of daily sessions?

126. When did Congress add the words *Under God* to the Pledge of Allegiance?

127. Which states did father and son, Henry and Augustus Dodge, represent while serving simultaneously in the Senate in the mid 19th century?

128. Who raises the flag above the House chamber to show it is in session?

129. What was so special about Rep. Yvonne Burke (D-Ca.) being granted maternity leave of absence in 1973?

130. How many Senators are up for re-election every two years?

131. What is historic about the catafalque on which Abraham Lincoln's casket rested while he lay in state in the Rotunda?

ANSWERS

123. Final legislation passed by the House and Senate.

124. The House wing.

125. The sergeant at arms.

126. 1954.

127. Henry from Wisconsin and Augustus from Iowa.

128. Documentarian pages.

129. It was the first time a member of Congress had given birth.

130. One third.

131. It has been used for others similarly honored in the Rotunda.

132. How did almost blind House Speaker Sam Rayburn manage to preside over proceedings?

133. When did the vice president's inauguration move from the Senate chamber to the same venue for the president's swearing-in?

134. The portrait bust of Vice President Henry Wilson was made by the same person who created the statue at the Lincoln Memorial.

135. Where did the columns from the east portico end up when removed in mid 20th century for extensions?

136. How many pounds of cast iron are in the ceiling of the Hall of Columns?

137. Which president startled Senators by walking into the chamber and addressing them from his former seat?

138. Guess the religious denomination of most members in the first Congress of the 21st century?

139. How do Representatives and Senators refer to each other's institutions?

ANSWERS

132. By relying on whispered advice from the parliamentarian and staffers.

133. 1937.

134. Daniel Chester French.

135. Outdoors, at the National Arboretum in northeast Washington, D.C.

136. Almost 250,000 lbs.

137. Harry Truman, acting on a lunchtime dare from his friends in the Senate.

138. Catholics.

139. They call them *The Other Body.*

140. What was the individual cost of the first Senate desks?

141. Three weeks after the British burned the Library of Congress inside the Capitol, this man offered to sell his library of 6,487 books as a replacement.

142. Which room is set aside for the president when he visits the Capitol?

143. How soon after Oklahoma was admitted to the Union did its two Senators take office?

144. When are family members allowed to sit in the House chamber?

145. Who is third in line to the presidency?

146. The first Speaker of the House came from this state.

147. Until what date did the Senate conduct all business in secrecy?

148. When were extensions made to the east front?

149. What is the effect of unanimous consent?

ANSWERS

140. $34.

141. Congress accepted Thomas Jefferson's offer, paying him $23,950.

142. The ornate President's Room in the Senate wing.

143. 30 days after admission as a State on 16 November 1907.

144. For the official swearing-in of members.

145. The president pro tempore of the Senate.

146. Frederick Muhlenberg came from Pennsylvania.

147. 1794.

148. 1958–62.

149. It quickens normal proceedings in the House and Senate.

150. Who sculpted the statue of Abraham Lincoln in the Rotunda?

151. Who accepts applications from teenagers for the highly competitive positions of Congressional pages?

152. Where is the burial place of the foremost painter of the Capitol?

153. Marble for the 28 columns in the Hall of Columns came from this State.

154. Who was the Democrat from Washington State who became the first woman to chair a House Appropriations subcommittee?

155. When was a $5 stamp first issued showing the head of the statue of *Freedom* above the dome?

156. Name the only president who died in the U.S. Capitol?

157. Which country donated the ivory gavel used by the Senate's presiding officer?

158. Who sculpted the portrait bust of Martin Luther King, Jr. in the Rotunda?

ANSWERS

150. Vinnie Ream, commissioned while still a teenager.

151. Senators and Representatives.

152. Glenwood Cemetery in Washington, D.C.

153. Massachusetts.

154. Julia Hansen in 1967.

155. 1923.

156. John Quincy Adams, 1848.

157. India.

158. John Wilson.

159. These three brothers won election to the U.S. Senate.

160. How high and heavy are the Columbus Doors?

161. Where is the stained glass window depicting George Washington?

162. High high over the east plaza is the top of the statue above the dome?

163. How soon after Hawaii was admitted to the Union did its two Senators take office?

164. The president walks west from the Crypt for this historic ceremony.

165. Why did Congressmen run from the House chamber on the eve of Abraham Lincoln's second inaugural?

166. What was landscape architect Frederick Law Olmsted's starting pay for work on the Capitol grounds in 1874?

167. Which organization was chartered by Congress to promote the history of the Capitol?

168. How did Hattie Caraway (D-Ark.) make history in 1932?

ANSWERS

159. John F. Kennedy (D-Mass.), Robert F. Kennedy (D-N.Y.), Edward M. Kennedy (D-Mass.).

160. 17 ft. high and 20 tons.

161. In the Senate dining room.

162. 288 ft.

163. Three days after admission as a State on 21 August 1959.

164. The presidential inauguration.

165. They mistook thunder for an explosion.

166. $2,000 per year.

167. The United States Capitol Historical Society.

168. She was the first female elected to a full Senate term.

169. What is the House Journal?

170. What celebrated quote from Daniel Webster was entombed with the cornerstone of the Capitol extension in 1851?

171. Name the Senator who retired at the age of 100.

172. This House Speaker was nicknamed "Uncle Joe".

173. Does the Senate have to confirm the president's nominee to be Architect of the Capitol?

174. Who said he would filibuster until the rose in his lapel wilted?

175. Why did a gym attendant block a Senator from running out to vote?

176. Why is one member of the cabinet always absent when the president delivers his State of the Union address?

177. What are members of the House forbidden to do while the Speaker addresses the House or puts a question?

ANSWERS

169. Minutes of official proceedings in the House.

170. "The Union of the United States of America stands firm and their Constitution still exists unimpaired."

171. Strom Thurmond (R-S.C.), in 2003.

172. Joseph Cannon, Republican, Speaker 1903–11.

173. Yes.

174. Sen. Wayne Morse (Ind-Ore.), who spoke for 6 hours 13 minutes.

175. Sen. Allen Ellender (D-La.) forgot he was wrapped in a towel.

176. To succeed to the presidency in the event of a catastrophic loss of life when all the others are killed or incapacitated.

177. Nobody can walk out or across the chamber.

THE WHITE HOUSE
Home of the U.S. Presidents,
from South Lawn, Washington, D.C.

PC-02095 • K66310

Shin Sung Souvenir Co., P.O. Box 70250
Washington, D.C. 20024-0250
info@shinsunginc.com

PLEASE DO NOT WRITE BELOW THIS LINE. SPACE RESERVED FOR U.S. POSTAL SERVICE.

178. When did Congress authorize a U.S. Capitol police force?

179. Where in the Senate chamber is the marble bust of the first vice president, John Adams?

180. Why was there a 31 ft. blank on the Rotunda frieze for more than 50 years?

181. Wild animals are believed to have made a meal of this former Congressman in Colorado in 1916.

182. What happened when a blind woman tried to take her guide dog into the Senate gallery in 1950?

183. When was the first telecast from the Capitol?

184. Which humorist said "Congress has been writing my material for years."?

185. Who was the first person awarded the Congressional Gold Medal?

186. Why was the Capitol evacuated shortly before President Reagan was to lie in state in the Rotunda?

ANSWERS

178. 1828.

179. Above the presiding officer's rostrum.

180. The height of the frieze had been miscalculated.

181. Jeremiah Haralson (R-Ala.).

182. The sergeant at arms broke the rules and let them in.

183. 12 February 1946 during Lincoln Day ceremonies.

184. Will Rogers.

185. George Washington.

186. A plane authorized to fly above developed radio problems that prevented it being tracked.

187. Who sculpted the Senate's marble portrait bust of President Zachary Taylor?

188. Which president revived the practice of verbally delivering the State of the Union address instead of sending it in writing?

189. When must the House elect a president?

190. What book did an admiral steal as a souvenir when the British burned the Capitol in 1814?

191. In what year did Rep. Preston Brooks of South Carolina beat Sen. Charles Sumner of Massachusetts into unconsciousness after an anti-slavery speech?

192. Guess the circumference of the Rotunda frieze.

193. When is a point of order made?

194. What is the oldest committee of Congress?

195. Who wrote *A Manual of Parliamentary Practice for the Use of the Senate of the United States?*

196. Who gave Congress replicas of the bells in London's Westminster Abbey?

ANSWERS

187. Nobody knows. It was purchased from descendants.

188. Woodrow Wilson.

189. When no candidate receives a majority of electoral college votes in a presidential election.

190. *Receipts & Expenditures U.S. for 1810.*

191. 1856, after Sumner singled out Brooks' relative, Sen. Andrew Butler, for particular scorn.

192. 300 ft.

193. In the House and Senate when someone challenges the rules of procedure.

194. The House Committee on Ways and Means.

195. Thomas Jefferson.

196. Britain's Ditchley Foundation, as a bicentennial gift in 1976.

197. In what year did the 26th Amendment lower the voting age to 18?

198. Who painted George Washington's portrait above the canopy in the Old Senate Chamber?

199. How are the flanking House and Senate Office Buildings connected to the Capitol?

200. What did Sen. Margaret Chase Smith (R-Me.) place on John F. Kennedy's former Senate desk after his assassination?

201. This lawyer was the first African-American elected to the Senate by popular vote.

202. What are the main daily tasks of House cloakroom pages?

203. If a Senator yields to another does that mean losing the right to continue speaking?

204. In which room did President Lyndon Johnson sign the historic Voting Rights Act of 1965?

205. Why did cost estimates for marble columns skyrocket from $1,550 to more than $5,000 each in the early 19th century?

ANSWERS

197. 1971.

198. Rembrandt Peale.

199. By tunnels.

200. A rose.

201. Edward William Brooke III (R-Mass.).

202. Fielding phone calls and messages for members on the floor.

203. No.

204. The President's Room.

205. Inexperienced, and often drunk and brawling quarrymen, working during floods and icy conditions with periodically impure marble.

206. Guess the square footage of the mural in the canopy of the dome above the Rotunda?

207. What did the Residence Act of 1790 mandate?

208. What was the first order of business in the Senate's very first session?

209. Charles Dickens was so horrified by "the universal disregard of the spittoon" when visiting the Senate in 1842 that he gave this advice.

210. He was Abraham Lincoln's first vice president before election to the Senate.

211. When was the restored Old Supreme Court Chamber opened to the public?

212. Guess how many bronze fillings closed the cracks and holes in the statue of *Freedom* when lowered to ground level in 1993?

213. From which country were the earliest stonecutters recruited to build the Capitol?

214. The left ear of this man's marble bust was twice damaged and repaired.

ANSWERS

206. 4,664 sq. ft.

207. That the federal capital would be in Philadelphia until 1800 when it would move to what is now Washington, D.C.

208. Adoption of standing rules.

209. Never to pick anything off the floor "with an ungloved hand."

210. Hannibal Hamlin.

211. 1975.

212. 700.

213. Scotland.

214. Former Senate President and later U.S. President Calvin Coolidge.

215. How many men worked in quarries beside the Potomac River to rebuild the Capitol in 1817?

216. Guess the dimensions of the Library of Congress burned by the British inside the Capitol.

217. Can Delegates from the District of Columbia, Guam, American Samoa, and the U.S. Virgin Islands vote in House committees?

218. Who was the first Asian/Pacific-American woman elected to Congress?

219. Who owned the land before the Capitol was built upon it?

220. A marble statue of this famous Mormon leader was the gift of Utah for Statuary Hall.

221. She made history with election to the Senate while still in the White House.

222. How many cases were heard by the Supreme Court in its first year in the Capitol?

223. What brought together the great grandchildren of Senators Henry Clay and John C. Calhoun?

ANSWERS

215. 122.

216. 86 ft. long, 35 ft. wide, and 36 ft. high.

217. Yes.

218. Patsy Takemoto Mink (D-Hi.), 1964.

219. Daniel Carroll of Duddington.

220. Brigham Young.

221. Hillary Rodham Clinton (D-N.Y.).

222. Ten.

223. The unveiling of the Senators' portraits in the Senate Reception Room, 1959.

224. The governor of this State appointed his daughter to fill the remainder of his term in the Senate.

225. The governor of this State appointed his wife to a vacancy in the Senate.

226. Where can you view the mural memorializing the crew of the space shuttle *Challenger?*

227. This president walked from his boarding house to the Capitol for his inauguration.

228. Imagine how many plants were stolen when the summer house opened on the grounds in 1880.

229. Where is Hawaii's statue honoring Father Damien for helping lepers before dying of the same disease?

230. Which party did Abraham Lincoln represent in Congress?

231. What major subterranean addition was built in the first few years of the 21st century?

232. Where was James Monroe inaugurated in 1817 while the Capitol was being rebuilt?

ANSWERS

224. Frank Murkowski (R-Aka.).

225. Edwin Edwards of Louisiana.

226. In the Senate wing's Brumidi Corridors.

227. Thomas Jefferson, 1801.

228. Over 3,000.

229. House connecting corridor, first floor.

230. The Whigs.

231. The Capitol Visitor Center.

232. At the Old Brick Capitol opposite the east front.

233. This unsuccessfully impeached president was later elected to the Senate.

234. Who ran the length of the Capitol en route to the White House, where he learned he had succeeded to the presidency?

235. Members of the House have to be at least this age.

236. How much were the first members of Congress paid?

237. Who finished painting *William Penn and the Indians* on the Rotunda frieze?

238. What is unique about New Jersey's Philip Kearny (1815–62) whose bronze statue is in the Hall of Columns?

239. Guess what operated the first traffic signal on the Capitol grounds when installed in 1921.

240. Who was the first American commissioned to make a sculpture for the Capitol?

241. Where did the House meet in 1949 and 1950 while its chamber was being remodeled?

242. What did George Washington think of the winning design for the Capitol?

ANSWERS

233. Andrew Johnson.

234. Harry Truman.

235. 25 years old.

236. $1,500 per year.

237. Filippo Costaggini, on the death of Constantino Brumidi in 1880.

238. He is the only U.S. citizen to have an equestrian statue over his grave at Arlington National Cemetery.

239. Gas.

240. Horatio Greenough, 1832, whose controversial, partially-clothed sculpture of George Washington, is now in the National Museum of American History in Washington, D.C.

241. In the spacious Ways and Means Committee room, Longworth House Office Building.

242. He praised its "grandeur, simplicity, and beauty."

243. Who was the only president inaugurated publicly in the Capitol's office of the vice president?

244. The Senate's oil portrait of this former president of the Continental Congress was painted while he was a prisoner in the Tower of London.

245. Why is the bust of disgraced Vice President Spiro Agnew in the Capitol?

246. When did Congress adopt the Great Seal of the United States?

247. This man was the only incumbent president to see his vice presidential bust dedicated.

248. Where is the burial site of Dr. William Thornton, who won the original design for the Capitol?

249. Why does one page have to be present on the floor during sessions?

250. Which official manages the office and staff of a House member who dies, resigns, or is expelled?

ANSWERS

243. Chester Arthur in 1881.

244. Henry Laurens.

245. Though he resigned, pleading no contest to tax evasion, he had been president of the Senate and entitled to have his portrait bust in the Senate's collection.

246. 1782.

247. George H.W. Bush.

248. Congressional Cemetery in Washington, D.C.

249. To be of service to any member.

250. The Clerk of the House.

251. How much did Congress pay Rembrandt Peale for his portrait of George Washington in the Old Senate Chamber?

252. Who was the first person to win election as a write-in candidate?

253. What do a select few House and Senate members do on a Conference Committee?

254. What gives the House and Senate authority to hold secret sessions?

255. Who provides replacement flags, when needed, behind the House Speaker's chair?

256. Are the chairs, sofas, and desks originals in the Old Senate Chamber?

257. Name the French city planner who envisioned an open Mall stretching west from the Capitol.

258. Who carved the bust of Gerald Ford for the vice presidential collection?

259. How many feet above sea level is the base of the Capitol?

ANSWERS

251. $2,000 in 1832.

252. Strom Thurmond of South Carolina in 1954.

253. Try to compromise on differences in specific legislation.

254. Article I section 5 of the Constitution.

255. The Daughters of the American Revolution.

256. No. They are reproductions of 1819 furniture.

257. Pierre L'Enfant in 1791.

258. Master stone carver Vincent Palumbo.

259. 88 ft.

260. Why were the marble terraces built on the west, north, and south in the late 19th century?

261. When were African-American journalists first admitted to the House and Senate press galleries?

262. The longest-serving Senate official said of this man, "I have never heard his equal as an orator."

263. Who publishes the daily *Congressional Record*?

264. Why was architect Benjamin Henry Latrobe against quickly rebuilding the Capitol after it was burned by the British?

265. This man sculpted illustrious Congressmen but is best known for creating the U.S. Marine Corps Memorial.

266. Why does the president deliver a State of the Union address to Congress?

267. What is the Hopper?

268. What famous Congressman was nicknamed Old Man Eloquent?

ANSWERS

260. The Capitol looked like it was about to slide off the hill.

261. 1947.

262. Sen. Henry Clay of Kentucky.

263. The government printing office.

264. He cautioned, "Rapid building is bad building."

265. Felix de Weldon.

266. Article II section 3 of the Constitution mandates the president do this "from time to time."

267. The container where bills are placed in the long process of perhaps becoming law.

268. Former president and later Rep. John Quincy Adams.

269. Where will you see two snuff boxes in the Senate?

270. How did Clerk of the Works John Lenthall lose his life in 1808?

271. Why does the statue above the dome face away from downtown Washington?

272. Why was the public banned from the Capitol 15 April 1865?

273. Why is the space within the Senate Rotunda called "Mark Twain's Cuspidor" (spittoon)?

274. What does a single short ring of bells indicate to Senators?

275. Guess the weight of the heaviest man elected to Congress in the 19th century?

276. What section of the Rotunda frieze was Constantino Brumidi painting when he died in 1880?

277. Guess the cost of the almost 9 million lbs. ironwork dome.

ANSWERS

269. Behind the presiding officer's rostrum.

270. Vaulting fell on him in the Old Supreme Court Chamber.

271. It faces the main entrance which is on level ground.

272. As a security measure the day President Lincoln died.

273. Because the columns are topped with tobacco leaves.

274. That they should enter their chamber to vote.

275. Sen. Dixon Hall Lewis (D-Ala.) weighed in excess of 400 lbs.

276. *William Penn and the Indians.*

277. Over $1 million.

278. When did Shirley Chisholm become the first African-American woman elected to Congress?

279. In what year was running water provided inside the Capitol?

280. What is the minimum age requirement for election to the Senate?

281. What prohibits members of Congress from voting themselves an immediate pay increase?

282. What were the votes in the House and Senate to declare war on Britain in 1812?

283. How much was John Trumbull paid for his four paintings in the Rotunda?

284. How many decades passed before Sen. Daniel Inouye (D-Hi.) received the Medal of Honor for an act of uncommon valor during World War II?

285. Where is the grave of 18th century Capitol architect George Hadfield?

286. Of what celebrated marble is the bust of Constantino Brumidi made?

ANSWERS

278. The New York Democrat was elected to the House in 1968.

279. 1832.

280. Thirty.

281. The 27th Amendment mandates an election of Representatives must first have intervened.

282. 79 to 49 in the House and 19 to 13 in the Senate.

283. $32,000.

284. Five and a half. The medal was presented by the president in the year 2000.

285. Congressional Cemetery in Washington, D.C.

286. Carrara marble.

287. When was the presidential inauguration first televised?

288. Who completed the Rotunda frieze?

289. Who takes messages from the president and Senate when the House is not in session?

290. When did Congress establish the Medal of Honor?

291. Who designed the dome?

292. Can a vacancy in the Senate be filled by appointment of a new member?

293. Where is the statue of the President of the Confederacy in the Capitol?

294. These three World War II wounded heroes became close friends during convalescence then won election to the Senate.

295. Where is the statue of Irish immigrant Sen. James Shields, the only man elected from three different States?

296. This Senator from Montana was a 14-year-old in the U.S. Navy in World War I then rose to be Senate majority leader during the Vietnam War.

ANSWERS

287. 1949.

288. Allyn Cox.

289. The Clerk of the House.

290. 1862.

291. Architect Thomas Walter.

292. Yes, but only for the remainder of the original term.

293. Jefferson Davis of Mississippi is in Statuary Hall.

294. Philip Hart (D-Mich.), Daniel Inouye (D-Hi.), and Bob Dole (R-Ks.).

295. In the Hall of Columns.

296. Democrat Mike Mansfield.

297. Where is William Powell's painting *The Discovery of the Mississippi by DeSoto 1541*?

298. Who was the last president sworn-in on the east front before the ceremony moved to the west front?

299. How many people were elected president of the Continental Congress?

300. Why did Congressman Davy Crockett call for the closure of the West Point Military Academy?

301. Which Congressman helped the teenager Bill Gates become a House page?

302. Thomas Jefferson called this man's winning design for the Capitol "simple, noble, beautiful."

303. On what West Indian island is Columbus depicted in the Rotunda painting *The Landing of Columbus*?

304. In which room are the acoustics so strange that a whisper can be heard clearly from 45 ft. away?

305. How many trees were on the Capitol grounds at the start of the 21st century?

ANSWERS

297. In the Rotunda.

298. Jimmy Carter.

299. Fourteen.

300. He said, "They are too delicate and cannot rough it in the army."

301. Brock Adams (D-Wash.).

302. Dr. William Thornton.

303. Guanahani, the Bahamas.

304. Statuary Hall, especially where Rep. John Quincy Adams sat.

305. 920.

306. Where are the portraits of George Washington's first cabinet?

307. Which assassin stalked Abraham Lincoln at his second inaugural?

308. When was the statue of Chief Justice John Marshall removed from the Capitol's west lawn to the Supreme Court?

309. Colorado honored this native son astronaut with a statue in the Capitol.

310. When the government moved to Washington in 1800 Congress shared this sole completed wing of the Capitol with the Supreme Court and Library of Congress.

311. What happened to the 18th century ivory gavel when Vice President Richard Nixon banged for order?

312. How many years must a person have been a U.S. citizen to validate election to the House?

313. How many years must a person have been a U.S. citizen to validate election to the Senate?

ANSWERS

306. In the President's Room, Senate wing.

307. John Wilkes Booth.

308. 1981.

309. John L. Swigert, Jr.

310. The original north wing.

311. It broke apart.

312. Seven years.

313. Nine years.

314. How come the House Appropriations Committee reported an annual salary of $3.5 million for the House chaplain?

315. Do the more than half a million residents of Washington, D.C. have representation in the U.S. Senate?

316. Who painted *The Embarkation of the Pilgrims at Delft Haven, Holland,* on view in the Rotunda?

317. Where is the original plaster model for the statue of *Freedom* atop the dome?

318. How did blind Sen. Thomas Gore (D-Ok.) tell time?

319. This female surgeon denied before the House Judiciary Committee in 1912 that Congress permitted her to wear men's clothing.

320. Why did Speaker Joe Cannon frantically keep the House in continuous session for 29 hours in 1910?

321. Senate pages must be high school juniors and at least this age.

ANSWERS

314. A typographical error added three zeroes.

315. No.

316. Robert Weir.

317. In the basement of the Russell Senate Office Building.

318. He pressed a button on his watch and listened to the tell-tale sounds of hours and minutes.

319. Civil War Medal of Honor recipient Dr. Mary Walker, who always wore pants.

320. His autocratic authority was challenged and he vainly held up a vote to curtail his powers.

321. 16 years old.

322. Guess when Hawaiian Henry Giugni became the first Polynesian appointed Senate sergeant at arms.

323. The father of the first man to fly solo across the Atlantic represented this State in Congress.

324. Where in the Senate are the words *E Pluribus Unum?*

325. How many books did Congress's library have two years after moving into the Capitol?

326. To which House committee do new members turn to for help in setting up offices?

327. An 1851 fire in the Capitol destroyed marble busts by Guiseppe Ceracci of these two early presidents.

328. How did a Senator speaking on the floor manage to keep the attention of legislators during a World Series opening game?

329. Who was the first vice president honored by the Senate with a bust?

ANSWERS

322. 1987.

323. Charles Lindbergh was a Republican Congressman from Minnesota.

324. Above the presiding officer's desk.

325. 964.

326. The Committee on House Administration.

327. George Washington and Thomas Jefferson.

328. During his 1940 speech he gave the inning by inning score between the Detroit Tigers and Cincinnati Reds.

329. Henry Wilson (R-Mass.), 1812–75.

330. In which chamber will you see a gilded eagle perched on a shield with 13 stars and stripes?

331. How do Senators traditionally mark the death of one of their members?

332. How much did Bill Clinton earn as assistant clerk on the Senate Foreign Relations Committee while an undergraduate at Georgetown University?

333. When was the presidential inauguration first transmitted worldwide by satellite?

334. How high above the Rotunda floor is the painting *Apotheosis of Washington?*

335. What were the last words of former President John Quincy Adams before he died in the Capitol?

336. Whose giant portraits are behind the Speaker's chair, to his left and right?

337. Where did Abraham Lincoln board as a one-term Congressman?

338. What are The Congress Bells?

ANSWERS

330. Above the presiding officer's chair in the Old Senate Chamber.

331. By adjourning the day's session.

332. $3,500 per year.

333. 1969.

334. 180 ft.

335. "This is the end of earth, but I am composed."

336. George Washington and the Marquis de Lafayette.

337. At Annie Sprigg's house opposite the Capitol's east front, where the Jefferson building of the Library of Congress stands today.

338. A British gift to Congress of replicas of bells in Westminster Abbey.

339. How long after their speeches are Senators given transcripts to make only minor changes?

340. Who was the first president to walk from the Capitol to the White House after his inauguration?

341. In 1870 he became the first African-American Senator, appointed to fill the unexpired term of former Sen. Jefferson Davis (D-Miss).

342. When did C-Span begin broadcasting proceedings of the House?

343. Who won the prize of $500 and a city lot for designing the Capitol?

344. When is the *Star-Spangled Banner* chimed at the Sen. Robert A. Taft Memorial bell tower near the Senate wing?

345. The Rotunda has two paintings of this famous Native American woman.

346. Which vice president appeared tipsy when taking the oath of office in the Senate chamber?

ANSWERS

339. Less than an hour.

340. Jimmy Carter.

341. Hiram Revels.

342. 1979.

343. Dr. William Thornton.

344. Every Fourth of July.

345. Pocahontas is in *The Baptism of Pocahontas* and on the frieze in *Captain Smith and Pocahontas.*

346. Andrew Johnson.

347. This disease killed the preeminent architect of the Capitol.

348. How did Representatives Daniel Sickles (D-N.Y.) and William Stone (D-Ky.) manage to vote in the 53rd Congress after each had lost a leg fighting on opposite sides in the Civil War?

349. What was The Soldiers' Roll?

350. Why are two figures deliberately obscured in Howard Chandler Christy's painting *The Signing of the Constitution of the United States*?

351. When was the House Mace crafted by a New York silversmith?

352. What prompted House Chaplain Rev. James Ford to play *The Saints Go Marching In* on his harmonica?

353. Why were cenotaphs memorializing deceased members of Congress no longer placed in Congressional Cemetery after 1877?

354. Which former president successfully lobbied Congress to move the Supreme Court out of the Capitol?

ANSWERS

347. Benjamin Henry Latrobe died of yellow fever in 1820.

348. Other Congressmen asked how they wanted to vote, then took a crutch from each man and made a show of holding them up while announcing the voting intentions of the amputees.

349. Lifetime jobs as House gallery doormen for a handful of Civil War veterans.

350. He could not find reliable portraits to work from of signers Jacob Broom, Delaware, and Thomas FitzSimons, Pennsylvania.

351. 1841.

352. Majority Leader Jim Wright was short of a player to entertain guests.

353. It was considered a costly waste of burial space.

354. William Howard Taft, when later Chief Justice.

355. Where in the Senate chamber can you see a relief of an ancient warrior tangling with a snake?

356. This former Senator won the Nobel Peace Prize in 1945.

357. What assistance does the Congressional Research Service give members of Congress?

358. This man represented the U.S. in judo at the 1964 Olympics before his election to the Senate.

359. Where are the marble busts of the first four Chief Justices?

360. Guess the cost of each of the nine desks purchased in the 1830s for Supreme Court justices.

361. What is the total acreage of the Capitol grounds?

362. By what method do members vote in the House?

363. What does a long ring of bells indicate to Senators?

ANSWERS

355. *Courage* is above the far west door on the presiding officer's right.

356. Cordell Hull (D-Tenn.).

357. Experts research for House and Senate members and their staffs.

358. Ben Nighthorse Campbell, a Colorado Democrat until switching to the Republican party in 1995.

359. In the Old Supreme Court Chamber.

360. $22 each. Six in the Old Supreme Court Chamber are believed to be originals.

361. 273 acres.

362. Electronically.

363. The opening of a daily session.

364. Who said he was entitled to the thanks of Congress for leaving it alone for 71 years?

365. Thomas Gore, 37, was the youngest Senator upon the admission of his State of Oklahoma to the Union, but how was he disabled?

366. What became of Capitol space occupied by the Library of Congress when it moved to its own building in 1897?

367. The Senate page residence is named in honor of this spellbinding 19th century orator.

368. How many people are in the mural *The Apotheosis of Washington* in the canopy of the dome?

369. Which four paintings in the Rotunda are by John Trumbull?

370. Why is one of every state's two Senators referred to as "the senior Senator"?

371. What is the duration of each Congress?

372. How tall is the statue of *Freedom* atop the dome?

ANSWERS

364. Humorist Mark Twain.

365. He was blind in both eyes from separate accidents during childhood.

366. It was converted into committee rooms.

367. Sen. Daniel Webster.

368. Fifty seven.

369. *The Declaration of Independence, Surrender of Cornwallis at Yorktown, Surrender of General Bourgoyne at Saratoga, General Washington Resigning His Commission as Commander-in-Chief.*

370. The one with the longest continuous service has the title.

371. Two years.

372. 19 ft. 6 in.

373. Who was the infamous Confederate camp commandant hanged in the shadow of the Capitol 10 November 1865?

374. Which House Speaker was nicknamed Cactus Jack?

375. Which Congressman charged with murder was the first American to raise the defense of temporary insanity?

376. This woman was elected to the House four years before the 19th Amendment guaranteed women the vote.

377. How long is a full term in the Senate?

378. When did the first office building open to accommodate House members outside the Capitol?

379. Walt Whitman described this conspicuous statue as a female "with drapery...and a face of good-natured indolent expression."

380. What was the first fresco painted in the Capitol by Constantino Brumidi?

381. This supervising engineer of the Capitol extension enjoyed catching snakes.

ANSWERS

373. Capt. Henry Wirz, in charge of Andersonville, Ga. prisoner of war camp, where an estimated 13,000 Union soldiers died of malnutrition, disease, exposure, and gunshots.

374. Texas Democrat John Nance Garner.

375. Rep. Daniel Sickles (D-N.Y.), who shot dead a son of Francis Scott Key.

376. Jeannette Rankin (R-Mont.) in 1916.

377. Six years.

378. 1908, now called the Cannon House Office Building.

379. *Freedom,* atop the dome.

380. *Calling of Cincinnatus from the Plow,* in Room H-144.

381. Montgomery Meigs.

382. How long after terrorists struck the second World Trade Center tower in New York was the Capitol evacuated?

383. What is the link between the Capitol and the bicentennial of the Lewis and Clark Expedition?

384. This *New York Times* reporter covered the Senate while writing a blockbuster novel about Washington politics titled *Advise and Consent.*

385. Guess the home State of the Congressman who had a collection of more than 100 bibles in 1950.

386. This naturalized American created the almost 14 ft. high bronze doors between the Crypt and the Memorial Door.

387. What coded words did 19th century Senators use when ordering pages to bring alcohol?

388. How many sessions are there normally in each Congress?

389. What historic event took place at the Capitol on Fourth July 1851?

ANSWERS

382. About 45 minutes.

383. The nickel commemorative coin has the Capitol as a backdrop.

384. Allen Drury.

385. Rep. Joseph Bryson (D-S.C.).

386. Italian-born Louis Amateis, who immigrated in 1844.

387. They ordered "cold tea."

388. One in each of the two years.

389. President Millard Fillmore laid the cornerstone of the Capitol extension.

390. When were radio reporters first given seats in the House and Senate galleries?

391. Which Senate official escorted the Queen of England to her car after she visited the Capitol for Bicentennial celebrations?

392. What is a filibuster, unique to the Senate?

393. What was the daily wage of the highest-paid artist in the Capitol by 1858?

394. Are spectators allowed to cheer, stomp, applaud, or talk in the House or Senate galleries?

395. In what year did Rep. Pete Sessions (R-Tx.) become the first Congressman to earn scouting's prestigious Wood Badge for advanced leadership training?

396. After painting *Cornwallis Sues For Cessation Of Hostilities,* the proud immigrant artist signed off this way.

397. When did Senate rules first allow for cloture votes to end debates?

398. How did President Andrew Jackson escape an attempted assassination in the Capitol?

ANSWERS

390. 1939.

391. The sergeant at arms.

392. Unlimited speech to avoid an issue being voted on.

393. $10 per day.

394. No.

395. 2004.

396. C Brumidi Artist Citizen of the U.S.

397. 1917.

398. The assailant's two pistols misfired.

399. When did television coverage of the House and Senate begin?

400. Which president almost micromanaged rebuilding of the Capitol 1818–19?

401. How many tons of marble for the Capitol were damaged in 1816 by inexperienced quarry workers?

402. When must Senators elect a vice president?

403. How did the Senate guard against leaks when debating funding for neutron bombs?

404. Why did President Grover Cleveland wear a single shoe at the inauguration of his successor?

405. Does a person have to be a resident of a State to represent it in Congress?

406. These two distantly-related Senators became president.

407. This marks the center of the Crypt.

408. Who are awarded Congressional Gold Medals?

ANSWERS

399. The House in 1979 and the Senate in 1986.

400. James Monroe.

401. More than 80 tons.

402. When no candidate receives a majority of electoral college votes in a presidential election.

403. It met behind closed doors in 1977.

404. He suffered from gout in 1897.

405. Yes.

406. John Tyler was the brother of Harry Truman's great-grandfather's father.

407. The compass stone.

408. Individuals and institutions honored as national appreciation for distinguished achievements and contributions.

409. Is public parking available on the Capitol grounds?

410. How does Congress traditionally welcome a newly-inaugurated president and vice president?

411. When did artist Allyn Cox finish painting the final scenes on the Rotunda frieze?

412. When did the Senate vote to acquit President Andrew Johnson of Impeachment charges?

413. When did the Senate vote to acquit President Clinton of impeachment charges?

414. What indicates whether the House is in session or in committee?

415. When did House members move into their current chamber?

416. When was the tradition begun of flying flags continuously over the Capitol's east and west fronts?

417. Who was the first vice president sworn into office in the Senate chamber after passage of the 25th Amendment?

ANSWERS

409. No.

410. With a lunch in Statuary Hall.

411. 1953.

412. 1868.

413. 1999.

414. The Mace on the Speaker's right is placed on a lower level when members are in Committee of the Whole House.

415. 1857.

416. During World War I.

417. Nelson Rockefeller in 1974.

418. Where did much of the stone come from to erect the Capitol?

419. In 1800 Congressmen failed to change this rule about chaplains.

420. Why did Congress get involved in the wedding of Gen. William Tecumseh Sherman's daughter?

421. Where does the Capitol Christmas Tree come from?

422. When did an armed intruder shoot dead two Capitol police officers?

423. Why was only one of the gas-burning chandeliers kept in the Capitol after a gas explosion in 1898?

424. Which Senator said his mother often told him how to vote?

425. What is the official title of stenographers recording speeches in the House and Senate?

426. Which House Speaker served longer than any of his predecessors?

ANSWERS

418. Quarries near Aquia Creek in Virginia.

419. That House and Senate chaplains be of different denominations.

420. Congress exempted her from paying $75,000 duties on the gift of a $300,000 diamond necklace from the Khedive of Egypt.

421. A different national forest every year.

422. 1998.

423. It was electrified and is now in the President's Room.

424. Harry Truman.

425. Official Reporters of Debate.

426. Sam Rayburn (D-Tx.) was Speaker for 17 years until his death in 1961.

427. How did Rep. Newton Curtis (R-N.Y.) lose an eye in the Civil War because of his height?

428. Senate pages scrambled for these souvenirs during World War I.

429. Who painted the heroic scene of Commodore Oliver Hazard Perry at the Battle of Lake Erie?

430. This ace fighter pilot during the Vietnam War resigned from Congress after admitting he took bribes.

431. When did the tradition die out of freshmen Senators lining up to take snuff?

432. Why was Gerald Ford sworn-in as vice president in the House chamber?

433. Which country made the decorative brass spittoons placed beside some Senate desks?

434. When were the flanking House Office Buildings opened?

435. When were the flanking Senate Office Buildings opened?

ANSWERS

427. Confederates tried firing over the attackers' heads to frighten them off but Curtis was nearly 7 ft. tall.

428. Discarded envelopes bringing messages from the president for the Senate.

429. William Powell in 1873.

430. Randy "Duke" Cunningham (R-Ca.). in 2005.

431. In the mid 20th century.

432. His wish, because he had served so long there as a Congressman and Republican leader.

433. Taiwan.

434. Cannon, 1908, Longworth, 1933, Rayburn, 1965.

435. Russell, 1909, Dirksen, 1958, Hart, 1982.

436. Why was Ronald Reagan's public inauguration in the Rotunda in 1985?

437. When did a female first preside over the Senate?

438. Congress convened for a rare 3rd session under this president.

439. What are the dimensions of the Rotunda frieze?

440. This Senate official drowned when the steamship *President* sank en route to England in 1841.

441. This eccentric Senator from Illinois sported a pink toupee, whiskers, and moustache.

442. When did two Congressmen brawl savagely with fire tongs and canes on the House floor?

443. Who was elected Speaker on his first day in Congress?

444. Where is the "well" of the House?

445. Why is the statue of *Freedom* above the dome topped with an eagle's head, feathers, and talons?

436. It was too cold for an outdoor ceremony.

437. 1932, with Hattie Caraway (D-Ark.) presiding.

438. Franklin Delano Roosevelt, from 3 January 1940 to 3 January 1941, when much of the world was at war.

439. 8 ft. 4 in. high and about 300 ft. in circumference.

440. The Chaplain, Rev. George Cookman.

441. John Hamilton Lewis, who served 1913–19, and 1931–39.

442. Roger Griswold and Matthew Lyon tangled in 1798.

443. Henry Clay of Kentucky.

444. In front of the rostrum, from where members may address the House if they don't wish to speak from the benches.

445. Then secretary of war, Jefferson Davis, vetoed the sculptor's original design showing headgear with the symbolic liberty cap, worn in ancient Rome by former slaves demonstrating their freedom.

446. Why was Swiss-born Albert Gallatin ousted after election to the Senate in 1793?

447. How long did artist Constantino Brumidi, 74, cling to a ladder when his chair slipped on scaffolding 58 ft. above the floor of the Rotunda?

448. When are The Congress Bells rung atop the Old Post Office building?

449. How many people witnessed Abraham Lincoln's first inaugural at the Capitol?

450. Why is a statue of Chief Washakie in the Capitol?

451. This first American astronaut to orbit the earth was elected to the Senate in 1974.

452. When were the monumental terraces built on the west front?

453. How did Congress react to the disputed presidential election of 1876?

454. From which land were the first sculptors hired to decorate the Capitol?

455 How did *The Turnip Congress* of 1948 get its name?

ANSWERS

446. He had lived in the U.S. 14 years but had not been a citizen for the minimum nine years.

447. Fifteen minutes. He died four months later.

448. At the opening and closing of Congress, on State occasions, and public holidays.

449. An estimated crowd of 10,000.

450. Wyoming honored the former U.S. Army scout for his peaceful overtures to the military and pioneering individuals.

451. John Glenn (D-Oh.).

452. In eight years, beginning 1884.

453. It empowered States to declare the validity of their electors and it made majorities in the House and Senate prerequisites to the voiding of any electoral ballots.

454. Tuscany, Italy.

455. President Truman called Congress back into session on his own State's Turnip Day.

456. How did Constantino Brumidi ascend 58 ft. above the floor of the Rotunda to paint the frieze?

457. Why did House members choose the president in 1824?

458. Accommodation was so scarce in Washington in 1800 that it was suggested these people would have to live "like monks in a monastery, crowded 10 or 20 in one house."

459. Vice President Alben Barkley's portrait bust was made by the son of a president of this foreign country.

460. Why was John Raker (D-Ca.) sworn-in as a Congressman at his residence on 7 January 1926?

461. What was the euphemism for House Speaker Sam Rayburn's Capitol hideaway where intimates met for drinks?

462. What happened to the American Elm tree planted on the Capitol grounds in memory of Martin Luther King, Jr.?

ANSWERS

456. His cage was hoisted up by a pulley.

457. None of the four contenders had a majority of electoral votes.

458. Members of Congress.

459. Sculptor Kalervo Kallio immigrated from Finland in 1949.

460. He was too ill for the ceremony at the Capitol and died two weeks later.

461. The Board of Education.

462. It died but was replaced.

463. Where did Congress first convene after the British burned the Capitol in 1814?

464. Why did President Woodrow Wilson take the oath of office privately in the President's Room in 1917?

465. How did Congress deny President Andrew Johnson nominations to the Supreme Court?

466. How did Congress honor Dr. Jonas Salk for his discovery of a vaccine against polio?

467. By tradition, both Senate floor leaders phone the president on this occasion.

468. When hired to paint in the Capitol, immigrant artist Constantino Brumidi was warned to expect many critics. Why?

469. How many years passed before the Capitol Christmas Tree of 1970 doubled in height?

470. Why was the Capitol evacuated on a spring day in 2005?

471. How did the president and Congress honor two Capitol police officers slain in the building by a gunman?

ANSWERS

463. In the undamaged Patent Office in Washington.

464. Inauguration Day fell on a Sunday.

465. The Judicial Circuits Act of 1866 automatically reduced the size of the Court upon a vacancy.

466. It awarded him the Congressional Gold Medal.

467. Just prior to adjourning sine die at the close of that Congress's final session.

468. Because native-born artists would be jealous of him.

469. 35 years, doubling from 40 ft. high to 80 ft. high.

470. A light plane entered restricted air space above.

471. They attended the memorial service beside the coffins in the Rotunda.

472. The Senate rejected two Supreme Court nominees of this 20th century president.

473. Who destroyed a Mace in the House?

474. Bill Clinton worked part-time for this Senator while an undergraduate at Georgetown University.

475. Where was the first cornerstone laid?

476. What is traditionally hung behind the president's lunch table in Statuary Hall after the inauguration?

477. When was the $2 stamp showing the east front of the Capitol first issued?

478. How did a folded copy of the *Congressional Globe* save the life of Rep. Charles Van Wyck when a thug stabbed him in 1861?

479. In what year did electric lamps replace gas on the terrace?

480. Which Senator recited the biblical book of Ecclesiastes to prolong a 16-hour filibuster against industrial legislation?

ANSWERS

472. Richard Nixon's nominees, Clement Haynsworth and G. Harold Carswell.

473. British troops at war with America in 1814.

474. Sen. William Fulbright (D-Ark.), chairman of the Foreign Relations Committee.

475. On the southeast corner of the original House wing.

476. One or two paintings of people, landscapes, or events of relevance to the inaugural theme.

477. 1923.

478. The blade slashed through his overcoat and jacket before being blunted by the *Globe.*

479. 1897.

480. Sen. Huey Long (D-La.), in 1935.

481. How did the first Senators want to address the nation's leader before the House objected?

482. Long-time 19th century assistant door-keeper Isaac Bassett said public officials were always on guard against these "crafty and treacherous people."

483. Where is the mural of bedridden, wounded Civil War Union troops hospitalized in the Rotunda?

484. Which legislator/lawyer was as famous for debates in the Senate as for his arguments in the Supreme Court below?

485. Where is the inscribed souvenir book taken by British Admiral George Cockburn during the burning of the Capitol in 1814?

486. Who proclaimed his "one ambition and my daily prayer is that I may live long enough to make beautiful the Capitol of the one country on earth in which there is liberty."

ANSWERS

481. *His Highness, The President of the United States, and Protector of their Liberties.*

482. Lobbyists, most of whom he said were "blackmailers."

483. In the Hall of Capitols, House wing.

484. Daniel Webster.

485. In the Rare Books Division, Jefferson building, Library of Congress.

486. Italian immigrant artist Constantino Brumidi.

487. What year did House members vote 63 times over 18 days before electing a Speaker?

488. What happened when a gunman in the gallery in 1932 demanded to address the House?

489. How much damage was done when anti-Vietnam War radicals exploded a device in the Capitol in 1971?

490. Who was the last president inaugurated in the House chamber?

491. In which room did the mesmerizing orators—Daniel Webster, Henry Clay, and John C. Calhoun—debate?

492. What deterred Sen. Norris Cotton (R.-N.H.) from carving his initials on his Senate desk?

493. Where are the bas reliefs of Moses, two Popes, a Rabbi, and Napoleon?

494. Where is the House press gallery?

495. Why was the number of statues in Statuary Hall limited to 48?

ANSWERS

487. 1849.

488. Former Marine, Rep. Melvin Maas (R-Minn.), received the Carnegie Silver Medal for catching the weapon after talking him into dropping it.

489. About $300,000.

490. Millard Fillmore, in 1850.

491. The Old Senate Chamber.

492. The memory of doing that as a child, when a teacher "blistered my backside with a strap."

493. Images of the famous lawmakers circle the upper walls of the House chamber.

494. Above the Speaker's chair.

495. Additional weight would have endangered the Hall's structure.

496. This flag can only be flown over Senate offices.

497. Which committee distributes invitations to presidential inaugurations at the Capitol?

498. Where are the portraits of the first five Senators selected as "outstanding" among all deceased Senators prior to 1959?

499. When were females first appointed House pages?

500. When were females first appointed Senate pages?

501. This one-time Republican presidential nominee served in the Senate while his son was a member of the House.

502. What lies beneath the Crypt in space intended as a tomb for George Washington?

503. When was a joint session of Congress first televised?

504. How did World War II influence illumination of the Capitol's exterior and dome?

505. Why was Congress called into an extraordinary night session on 2 April 1917?

496. A blue flag with the Senate seal.

497. The Joint Committee on Inaugural Ceremonies.

498. In the Senate Reception Room adjoining the chamber. The five are Daniel Webster (Mass.), Henry Clay (Ky.), John C. Calhoun (S.C.), Robert La Follette (Wisc.), and Robert Taft (Oh.).

499. 1973.

500. 1971.

501. Sen. Barry Goldwater (R-Az.) and his son, Barry Goldwater, Jr. (R-Ca.).

502. The catafalque—a bier of boards covered with black cloth, first used to support the remains of Abraham Lincoln when his body lay in state.

503. 3 January 1947.

504. From 9 December 1941 until 9 May 1945 all searchlights, floodlights, terrace lights, and cluster lights were turned off.

505. President Wilson asked for a declaration of war against the Central Powers.

506. What more than doubled the length of the Capitol in the mid 19th century?

507. Portraits of this European monarch and his spouse decorated the walls during President John Adams's first address to Congress in Washington in 1800.

508. Who created the bronze Columbus Doors illustrating scenes from the life of the explorer?

509. What caused an explosion in 1898 leading to $50,000 worth of damage to the old north wing?

510. How does Congress intervene if a vice president dies, resigns, or is otherwise incapacitated?

511. The only incumbent Senator to die in combat during active service represented this State.

512. Where are the 16 sandstone columns topped with tobacco leaves?

513. In 1824 Congress honored this Frenchman with the first official reception in the Rotunda.

ANSWERS

506. The new House and Senate wings.

507. French King Louis XVI and Marie Antoinette, whose portraits had been presented by the monarch to the Continental Congress.

508. Randolph Rogers.

509. Leaking gas.

510. The president nominates a new vice president, who must be confirmed by a majority of both the House and Senate.

511. Sen. Edward Baker (R-Ore.) was killed in action at the Battle of Ball's Bluff 1861.

512. In the Small Senate Rotunda.

513. The Marquis de Lafayette.

514. How many barrels of flour were stored at one time in the Capitol to feed Union troops camped inside during the Civil War?

515. Where are the unique corn-cob capitals in the Senate wing?

516. Where did Congress convene for four years after the British burned the Capitol in 1814?

517. Why did Sen. John C. Calhoun want to reject the $500,000 gift of an Englishman to found the Smithsonian Institution?

518. Who was the first president inaugurated on the Capitol's west front?

519. Which abolitionist Senator was beaten mercilessly in the Senate chamber by an enraged Southern Congressman?

520. On what grounds was Rep. Philemon Herbert (D-Ca.) found not guilty of murdering a Washington hotel waiter in mid 19th century?

521. Who was the only former president later elected to the House?

ANSWERS

514. 13,000 barrels.

515. In the vestibule leading into the Old Supreme Court Chamber.

516. In a temporary Old Brick Capitol on the site of today's Supreme Court building.

517. He said it made the United States look like it couldn't afford it, or was too mean to spend its own money on the project.

518. Ronald Reagan.

519. Sen. Charles Sumner of Massachusetts.

520. He pleaded self defense in the fracas that began when the waiter said he arrived too late to be served breakfast.

521. John Quincy Adams.

522. How many terms did Abraham Lincoln serve in the House?

523. How was the Senate Democratic leader's office door blown off its hinges in 1983?

524. Who sits at the long desk in front of the Senate's presiding officer?

525. In which century did the annual pay for members of the House and Senate top $100,000?

526. Where is Rembrandt Peale's portrait of George Washington?

527. Why was Daniel Webster so proud of his memory?

528. Who are the three leaders of the women's rights movement depicted in the marble monument in the Rotunda?

529. Of what material is the dome constructed?

530. Until 1894 the U.S. flag flew only over these sections of the Capitol.

531. The current dome replaced a copper-covered wooden dome designed by this Boston architect.

ANSWERS

522. One, 1847–49.

523. Explosives set off by radicals protesting the invasion of Grenada.

524. Chief clerk, legislative clerk, parliamentarian, and journal clerk.

525. In the last decade of the 20th century.

526. Above the canopy and gilded eagle in the Old Senate Chamber.

527. He said he could prepare and revise speeches in his head, then deliver them from memory.

528. Elizabeth Cady Stanton, Susan B. Anthony, and Lucretia Mott.

529. Iron.

530. Over the House and Senate chambers.

531. Charles Bulfinch.

532. What happened immediately after Vice President Alben Barkley told a university audience, "I would rather be a servant in the house of the Lord than sit in the seats of the mighty."?

533. How much was Constantino Brumidi paid for painting *The Apotheosis of Washington?*

534. Which member of Knute Rockne's winning 1929 and 1930 Notre Dame football team became Senate sergeant at arms?

535. What riveted the audience during a 1932 speech by Rep. Edward Eslick (D-Tenn.)?

536. Does the House or Senate vote on presidential nominations to the Supreme Court?

537. How are members alerted to make up a quorum for a vote in the House?

538. Why was poet Robert Frost unable to read the poem written for President Kennedy's inauguration?

539. Who was the first member of either House or Senate to begin and successfully complete studies for a law degree, all the while being a member of Congress?

ANSWERS

532. He dropped dead, 30 April 1956.

533. $40,000.

534. Nordy Hoffman, 300 lbs. former tackle and guard.

535. He dropped dead on the floor of the House.

536. The Senate.

537. Bells ring in their wing of the Capitol and in their office buildings.

538. There was a blinding reflection from sunshine on the snow so he recited another from memory.

539. Robert Byrd (D-W.Va.), who graduated *cum laude* from American University in 1963 after 10 years of night classes.

540. Which country's parliamentary system of government most influenced procedures, protocol, and etiquette in Congress?

541. This architect beautified the Capitol before and after the British burned it in 1814.

542. This longest-serving Speaker of the House was posthumously awarded the Congressional Gold Medal "for services rendered to the people of the U.S."

543. Who died in the Vice President's Room minutes after declaring, "If I live to the close of my present term there will be only five who have served their country as long as I."?

544. Why did the Senate declare a seat vacant in 1975 and authorize a new election in New Hampshire?

545. Statues of these two presidents are close to the western perimeter of the grounds.

546. What criteria did each State have to meet to place two statues of its deceased citizens in Statuary Hall?

ANSWERS

540. Britain, notably with its House Speaker, sergeant at arms, Mace, committees, and legislative etiquette.

541. Benjamin Henry Latrobe.

542. Sam Rayburn (1882–1961).

543. Vice President and former Senator Henry Wilson, in 1875.

544. To end wrangling over recounts, where two votes separated the contestants.

545. James Garfield and Ulysses S. Grant.

546. The 1864 legislation said the statues had to be of citizens "illustrious for their historic renown or for distinguished civic or military services."

547. What is the difference between both houses of Congress assembling in joint session or for a joint meeting?

548. By what year did vice presidential portrait busts fill all available niches in the Senate's gallery walls?

549. When did African-American troops participate for the first time in an inaugural march between the Capitol and White House?

550. Who took over painting the Rotunda frieze after Constantino Brumidi died in 1880?

551. Who was esteemed as "the conscience of the Senate" and had a building named after him during his lifetime?

552. Where was Vice President Chester Arthur sworn in after the death of President Garfield?

553. Who took custody of the few books owned by Congress when the government moved to Washington in 1800?

ANSWERS

547. They are in joint session when the president addresses them, and in a joint meeting for other dignitaries.

548. 1898.

549. 1865.

550. Filippo Costaggini.

551. Sen. Philip Hart (D-Mich.), after whom the Hart Senate Office Building is named.

552. In the Vice President's office, Senate wing.

553. The Clerk of the Senate.

554. What disease killed the great early architect of the Capitol, Benjamin Henry Latrobe?

555. What was historic about the 6th Congress 2nd Session?

556. Which House committee assigns office space to members?

557. What is the House Journal?

558. Congress resolved to set aside "a room for prayer and meditation" for members in this year.

559. What prompted permanent employment of physicians in the Capitol?

560. Why did Congressmen discontinue allowances for summer interns in 1968?

561. Which Congressional staff are known as Runners?

562. What is so conspicuous in the ceiling of the House chamber?

563. How long did the Supreme Court meet in what is now the Old Supreme Court Chamber?

ANSWERS

554. Yellow fever.

555. Members convened for the first time in Washington.

556. The Committee on House Administration.

557. The constitutionally-mandated daily log of floor proceedings.

558. 1954.

559. The demise of an aged Congressman in his office in 1928.

560. One hundred and seventy nine interns had mailed anti-Vietnam War protests to the president.

561. Pages who make deliveries on Capitol Hill.

562. It has the seals of every State, Territory, and the District of Columbia.

563. For half a century from 1810.

564. What was Statuary Hall used for until 1857?

565. This Speaker ordered bean soup served daily in the House restaurant.

566. Why did the Senate sergeant at arms and others forcibly drag a Senator from his office into the Senate chamber in 1988?

567. How did Jane Grey Swisshelm make history in the Capitol on 17 April 1850?

568. In a tumultuous debate on slavery this Mississippian drew a pistol on Sen. Thomas Benton of Missouri.

569. When this wartime leader addressed a joint meeting of Congress, the House Speaker called him "one of the most distinguished figures on earth."

570. In 1975 this fitness freak Senator ran around the entire perimeter of his home State of Wisconsin.

571. Why did a reporter shoot dead a former Congressman in the Capitol in 1890?

ANSWERS

564. It was the Hall of the House of Representatives, where legislative proceedings took place.

565. Joe Cannon.

566. The Senate voted this rare action to make up a quorum.

567. She became the first female reporter in the Senate press gallery, writing for the *New York Tribune.*

568. Henry Foote was forcibly disarmed by colleagues.

569. British Prime Minister Winston Churchill, in 1943.

570. Democrat William Proxmire.

571. In self defense, when they tangled over a news account of the legislator's private life.

572. How did Pennsylvania Sen. Boies Penrose, 6 ft. 4 in. and 400 lbs, get an innocent bystander out of the way to enter an elevator?

573. How were the rules bent in 1888 for a sickly Senator?

574. How many of the 36 Senators voted in 1815 in favor of the Treaty of Peace and Amity ending the War of 1812?

575. Why are House and Senate parliamentarians so vital to Congress?

576. As of the beginning of the 21st century, which Senator held the record for longest filibuster?

577. This physically powerful Senator from Missouri had his servant scrub him down with a horse-hair brush twice a day to emulate the custom of Roman gladiators.

578. What title is given to the Senate's presiding officer, substituting for an absent vice president who is also president of the Senate?

ANSWERS

572. He picked him up and dumped him on the side.

573. Joseph Brown (D-Ga.) was allowed to sit while delivering his speech.

574. All 35 present. A vacancy from North Carolina had not yet been filled.

575. Their expert knowledge on rules, procedures, and precedents guide presiding officers in both chambers.

576. Strom Thurmond (R-S.C.) spoke for 24 hours 27 minutes against civil rights legislation.

577. Democrat Thomas Hart Benton, who died in 1858 at the ripe old age of 76.

578. Senate president pro tempore, normally the longest-serving Senator from the majority party.

579. What publication briefly recorded the first three dozen years of Congressional proceedings?

580. How many books were destroyed when British troops burned the Capitol's Congressional library in 1814?

581. Which distinguished Senator gave 14 one-hour speeches over five months in 1993 and later published them as a book titled *The Senate of the Roman Republic:Addresses on the History of Roman Constitutionalism.*?

582. Which Capitol official is responsible for maintenance of the buildings housing Congressional offices, the Library of Congress, and the Supreme Court?

583. How many varieties of trees and bushes are there around the Capitol?

584. When this Senator from Florida died in 1989 he was given the rare honor of lying in state in the Rotunda.

585. This renowned 19th century Senator from South Carolina died in 1850 in his boarding house, located on the site of today's Supreme Court building.

ANSWERS

579. *Annals of Congress.*

580. Over 3,000.

581. Robert Byrd (D-W.Va.).

582. The Architect of the Capitol.

583. More than one hundred.

584. Claude Pepper, Democrat.

585. John C. Calhoun of South Carolina.

586. Guess the nationality of a diplomat who wrote in 1805 that only about five Congressmen looked like gentlemen.

587. Where did James Madison twice take the presidential oath of office?

588. Name the Senate majority leader who was the son-in-law of Senate minority leader Everett Dirksen.

589. Where is the statue of Texas legend Sam Houston?

590. Who was the former Senator from Louisiana hauled off a British ship taking him on a Confederate mission to Europe?

591. What 19th century abuse of mailing privileges led to curtailment of this Congressional perk?

592. How did songsters in the House press gallery celebrate the end of a wearying session in 1891?

593. How did the House doorman startle the future Queen of England and her husband?

ANSWERS

586. British.

587. In the Hall of the House of Representatives, now called Statuary Hall.

588. Howard Baker (R-Tenn.).

589. In Statuary Hall.

590. John Slidell.

591. Congressmen were mailing their dirty clothing for cheaper laundering in their home towns.

592. They sang *Praise God From Whom All Blessings Flow.*

593. He greeted her, "Howdy Ma'am" then, from the rostrum called down, "Hey, pass me up the prince."

594. Why did a former radio announcer secretly install a deafening amplifier in the chamber after his election to the House in 1935?

595. This ailing Senator slipped into a coma and died a few hours after his crucial proxy vote was counted.

596. What did then Senate majority leader Lyndon Johnson do with a souvenir brick saved from the Capitol burned by the British in 1814?

597. How many weeks was *Advise and Consent,* Allen Drury's novel of Capitol intrigue, on the *New York Times* bestseller list?

598. Did the Supreme Court return to the Capitol before Congressmen after fires set by the British in 1814?

599. Who designed the unique corn-cob capitals in the vestibule leading into the Old Supreme Court Chamber?

600. From which room did President Lincoln demand Robert E. Lee's unconditional surrender?

ANSWERS

594. It was a practical joke.

595. Sen. Richard Russell (D-Ga.), whose vote helped Sen. Robert Byrd win election as Senate Democratic Whip in 1971.

596. He cemented it in the ground near the kitchen door of his Washington D.C. home and left it there after selling the house.

597. 93 weeks.

598. Yes, in temporary quarters while rebuilding continued.

599. Architect Benjamin Henry Latrobe.

600. The President's Room, 3 March 1865.

601. When did the 18th Amendment outlaw the manufacture, transportation, and sale of alcoholic beverages?

602. When was the 18th Amendment repealed by the 21st Amendment?

603. Have all the States given their maximum two statues to Statuary Hall?

604. How long is the widest part of the Capitol?

605. How long is the Capitol?

606. How did the House recognize the contribution of Scottish-Americans?

607. When can a House member claim a point of personal privilege?

608. What is a Whip?

609. Which committee oversees security in the House wing?

610. How much money did Congress vote to start its own library?

611. Which area of the Capitol has been occupied the longest?

ANSWERS

601. 1918.

602. 1933.

603. Yes.

604. 350 ft.

605. 751 ft. 4 in.

606. By passage of a National Tartan Day resolution.

607. To reply to personal remarks against character, conduct, and rights.

608. Each party elects a Whip to round up votes for that party's line.

609. The Committee on House Administration.

610. $5,000.

611. The northwest area of the original Senate wing.

612. What is significant about the location of the Senate majority leader's suite of offices?

613. Where in the Senate chamber are the words *In God We Trust?*

614. The atrium of the Hart Senate Office Building has a monumental sculpture by this famous 20th century sculptor.

615. Why was Room S-238 named after Sen. Strom Thurmond (R-S.C.) in 1997?

616. A year after Lincoln's assassination the House accepted his portrait in mosaic from a citizen of this country.

617. This former House Republican leader became the only unelected vice president and president.

618. Gerrymandering is named after this Senate President who, while Governor of Massachusetts, re-drew the perimeters of voting districts to benefit his party.

619. Did the Senate convict or acquit the first associate justice of the Supreme Court to be impeached?

ANSWERS

612. It is on the site of the original Library of Congress.

613. Above the south central door.

614. Alexander Calder's *Mountain and Clouds.*

615. That year he had served a record-breaking more than 41 years in the Senate.

616. Italy.

617. Gerald R. Ford, Jr.

618. Vice President Elbridge Gerry.

619. It acquitted Samuel Chase in 1805.

620. Which president cast the most vetoes over Congressional legislation?

621. When did the Senate elect the vice president?

622. Where is Pierre L'Enfant's original plan for the city of Washington and location of the Capitol?

623. How is Puerto Rico represented in Congress?

624. Where was Vice President Harry Truman when summoned to the White House to assume the presidency?

625. Where is the subterranean Capitol Visitor Center?

626. In 2000 the Senate voted to add portraits of these two lawmakers from Michigan and New York to its Reception Room gallery of outstanding Senators.

627. The outdoor concert on Fourth of July is traditionally on this part of the Capitol's grounds.

ANSWERS

620. Franklin Delano Roosevelt, the only president elected to four terms, used the veto 635 times.

621. In 1837 it elected Richard Johnson under the 12th Amendment because none of the candidates had received a majority of votes.

622. In the Library of Congress.

623. By a Resident Commissioner elected to a four year term.

624. In House Speaker Sam Rayburn's private office in the Capitol.

625. Under the east plaza.

626. Arthur Vandenberg (R-Mich.) and Robert Wagner (D-N.Y.).

627. The west lawn.

628. How did an Austrian immigrant create a link between Elvis Presley and House Speaker Sam Rayburn?

629. How did city planner Pierre L'Enfant refer to the Capitol before it was built?

630. What made President James Monroe congratulate Congressmen at the end of 1819?

631. What was significant about the calendar dates of the 106th Congress?

632. When was the restored Old Senate Chamber opened?

633. What major buildings face the Capitol's east front?

634. Why did work continue on the dome during the Civil War, even though the government suspended payment?

635. What was Daniel Webster's nickname?

636. What is the status of an enrolled bill?

637. What committee has jurisdiction over the official conduct of all House members?

628. Felix de Weldon sculpted likenesses of both men, one for Presley's mansion and the other for the Rayburn House Office Building.

629. In correspondence with George Washington 22 June 1791 he called it "the Congressional building."

630. They were back in the rebuilt Capitol, burned by the British in 1814.

631. It was the first to enter the year 2000.

632. 1976.

633. The Supreme Court and Jefferson building of the Library of Congress.

634. The contractor figured he had too much ironwork on site, which could not be abandoned.

635. "Old Roman".

636. Both the House and Senate have approved it and it is sent to the president.

637. The Committee on Standards of Official Conduct.

638. Was anyone killed when Puerto Rican terrorists opened fire in the House chamber in 1954?

639. What happened to a Constitutional Amendment proposed by a House member in 1911 to abolish the Senate?

640. Who are "lame duck" members of Congress?

641. Who was the first president to ride from the White House to the Capitol for his inauguration?

642. Why was there no inaugural parade from the Capitol to the White House in 1985?

643. After a House member dies, resigns, or is expelled, can the staff in the vacant office take or advocate positions of public policy before a new member is elected?

644. Senate Chaplain Dr. Richard Halverson had this unlikely employment before ordination.

ANSWERS

638. No, but five Congressmen were wounded.

639. It died in committee where no action was taken.

640. Those returning for the completion of a session following their defeat in earlier elections.

641. Thomas Jefferson, in 1805.

642. The parade was cancelled due to extreme cold.

643. No. The staff can only assist constituents with general information on the status of legislation, but cannot give analysis or opinions.

644. He performed in vaudeville.

645. How many wagons did Thomas Jefferson estimate would be required to transport his library to Washington if Congress accepted his offer to sell his 6,487 books?

646. This daughter of a president set one of her murder mystery novels in the Capitol.

647. What was the vote tally when the Senate rejected the Supreme Court nomination of Judge Robert Bork in 1987?

648? Why did the Equal Rights Amendment not become part of the Constitution after it received the required two-thirds approval by Congress in 1972?

649. How long did it take Constantino Brumidi to paint the fresco *Apotheosis of Washington* in the canopy of the dome?

650. What makes the Minton floor tiles enduringly vivid and lustrous?

651. When did the 17th Amendment take effect, providing for election of Senators by popular vote?

ANSWERS

645. Eighteen to twenty wagons.

646. Margaret Truman.

647. Yeas 58, nays 42.

648. Because it was not ratified by three-quarters of the States.

649. Eleven months.

650. Layers of colored clay are within the ordinary clay.

651. 1913.

652. Capitol Architect Benjamin Henry Latrobe rhapsodized over this sculptor's "first rate excellence."

653. Where is a conspicuous example of sculptor Giovanni Andrei's sculptural brilliance?

654. Who was the army engineer and superintendant of the Capitol extensions who also became Quartermaster General under President Lincoln?

655. Which politicians are taunted as carpetbaggers?

656. What are the most dignified tasks assigned to the House sergeant at arms?

657. Why did House Speaker Sam Rayburn ban television from House committees and floor debates?

658. This president took his oath of office at the Capitol with one hand on two family bibles printed in 1828 and 1873.

659. Why is a statue of the author of *Ben Hur* in the Capitol?

ANSWERS

652. He was referring to Giovanni Andrei.

653. He carved the columns in the vestibule at the entrance to the Old Supreme Court Chamber.

654. Montgomery Meigs.

655. Newcomers running for office in non-native States.

656. To announce the arrival of the president for the State of the Union address and to carry the Mace into the chamber for the start of daily proceedings.

657. He was upset by the televised reporting of a disorderly session of the House and of a committee meeting.

658. Richard Nixon, in 1969.

659. Indiana honored the author, Gen. Lew Wallace, as one of its distinguished citizens.

660. When was legislation passed to fly the U.S. flag over the east and west fronts of the Capitol?

661. Why is one of the desks in the Senate chamber not topped with mahogany writing boxes?

662. How did a Union soldier vandalize the Senate desk occupied by Confederate President Jefferson Davis when he was a U.S. Senator from Mississippi?

663. By tradition this is the first order of House business when a new Congress convenes.

664. Which official is charged with enforcing rules of the House?

665. Who was Architect of the Capitol when the outer wings were added?

666. Known as *the father of Alaska statehood,* this Senator's ashes were scattered over a mountain named after him in that State.

667. What became of the Old Supreme Court Chamber when the justices moved upstairs into the Old Senate Chamber?

ANSWERS

660. 1894.

661. Daniel Webster did not want this addition to his desk.

662. He stabbed it with his bayonet, gouging out a piece of wood.

663. Election of a Speaker.

664. The sergeant at arms.

665. Thomas Walter.

666. Democrat Ernest Gruening, who died 1974.

667. It was converted into a law library and reading room.

668. What did the 20th Amendment section 2 mandate?

669. Do bills to raise revenue have to originate in the House or Senate?

670. When did Senators move into their current chamber?

671. When was an elevator first in use in the Capitol?

672. Why did the remains of 18th century city planner Pierre L'Enfant lie in state in the Rotunda as late as 1909?

673. Where are electoral ballots counted after presidential elections?

674. When were major extensions made to the east front?

675. This noted 19th century landscape architect transformed the Capitol grounds with a profusion of plants and trees.

676. By eerie coincidence, all the gas lights on the west front of the Capitol blacked out within minutes of this man's assassination.

ANSWERS

668. That Congress should assemble at least once a year beginning at noon on 3 January, unless it chose a different date.

669. The House. The Senate can propose or concur with amendments.

670. 1859.

671. 1874.

672. The belated honor was accorded before his remains were reinterred in Arlington National Cemetery.

673. In the House chamber.

674. 1958–62.

675. Frederick Law Olmsted.

676. The night Abraham Lincoln was shot.

677. Guess the length of the Capitol Hill restroom built in 1800 for Congressmen arriving in the brand new federal capital.

678. Why did John A. Washington refuse to allow the remains of his great uncle George Washington to be buried in the Capitol?

679. What incident made Senators change the rules to allow guide dogs into the chamber?

680. Capitol architect Benjamin Henry Latrobe believed ecstatically that this would bring "native magnificence" to the Capitol.

681. How did British troops start the fires that burned much of the Capitol in 1814?

682. How did 19th century Senators inventively finish their sessions so they would not have to return to Washington to complete business?

683. Known affectionately as "Mister Sam", this Texas Democrat held office as House Speaker for a record 17 years.

ANSWERS

677. Seventy feet long.

678. Because George Washington's will stipulated that he should be buried on the grounds of his estate, Mount Vernon.

679. A visually-impaired senatorial aide was not allowed to bring her guide dog onto the floor in 1997.

680. Multicolored stone he found for columns in the House and Senate.

681. They lit the combustible content of their Congreve rockets, which they had spread over piles of furniture and fragments of doors and window frames.

682. They ordered a staffer to turn back the minute hand of the Senate clock to beat the noon deadline.

683. Sam Rayburn.

684. Though Congress convened in the Old Brick Capitol 1815–1819, the building became more famous as this during the Civil War.

685. On what rare occasions does the vice president exercise his constitutional right of presiding over the Senate?

686. When was the first electric monorail subway installed from the Russell Senate Office Building to the Capitol?

687. How did partially-deaf Rep. Leonard Schuetz (D-Ill.) get his hearing fully restored in 1940?

688. How did the luck of the Irish save Rep. Tip O'Neill from being killed during a 1954 terrorist attack in the House chamber?

689. What determines the number of Congressmen elected by each State?

690. How do Senators know the daily session has ended?

691. Where was the first attempt to assassinate a president?

ANSWERS

684. A prison holding, among others, notorious Confederate spies and those suspected of complicity in Lincoln's assassination.

685. To break anticipated tie votes.

686. 1912.

687. Another Congressman roared so loudly into the microphone during debate.

688. Bullets fired by Puerto Rican terrorists slammed into O'Neill's seat moments after he got up to leave the chamber.

689. The size of the State's population.

690. There are four short rings of the Senate bells.

691. In the Rotunda, 1835, with Andrew Jackson as the target.

692. Who painted the 20 ft. by 30 ft. mural *Westward The Course of Empire Takes Its Way?*

693. How many females had covered Congress from the press gallery before women were temporarily barred in 1880?

694. How many years must a person have been a U.S. citizen to validate election to the House?

695. What is the minimum age requirement for election to the House?

696. Wisconsin honored this French Jesuit missionary and explorer by donating his statue to the Capitol.

697. What was the last State to get full representation in Congress in the 20th century?

698. Which official has the distinction of announcing the arrival of the president for the State of the Union address?

699. Exposed to extreme cold during his two-hour inaugural address, this president died a month later.

ANSWERS

692. German-born Emanuel Leutze, during the Civil War.

693. Twenty.

694. Seven years.

695. Twenty five years old.

696. James Marquette (1637–75).

697. Hawaii.

698. The House sergeant at arms.

699. William Henry Harrison, 1841.

700. Why was the hole punched through the Crypt's ceiling permanently sealed in 1828?

701. How long has the portrait of the Marquis de Lafayette, behind the Speaker's rostrum, been in the House?

702. The New Yorker who painted the final scenes on the Rotunda frieze studied at this prestigious Italian academy.

703. How many people had been Architect of the Capitol by the end of the 20th century?

704. Where is the portrait bust of Martin Luther King, Jr.?

705. Which three states elected Irish immigrant and Democrat James Shields to the Senate from 1849 to 1879?

706. Which is the best place to see all 100 Senators if the public galleries are full?

707. Apart from the White House, where did 19th century fashionable Washingtonians congregate most?

ANSWERS

700. Because a statue of George Washington, intended to be visible from the Rotunda above, was never placed there.

701. Since the idolized Frenchman made a triumphal visit to Washington in 1824.

702. Allyn Cox was a student at the American Academy in Rome.

703. Ten.

704. In the Rotunda.

705. Illinois, Minnesota and Missouri.

706. At the top of escalators near the subways as Senators arrive for crucial votes.

707. Inside the Capitol.

708. Which Senator from West Virginia was seldom without a copy of the Constitution?

709. Why did Senate President Harry Truman finally take out a long lease on an apartment in Washington, a city he disliked?

710. Where will you see quill pens from the earliest days of the Capitol?

711. What is the distance between the Capitol and the Lincoln Memorial?

712. What is a select committee of the House or Senate?

713. What legislation mandated two copies of copyrighted new books to be deposited in the Library of Congress?

714. How was the House lit for evening sessions before the advent of gas?

715. If a House member yields to allow a colleague to speak, is that time subtracted from the time given the yielder?

716. What is the weight of the heaviest of the ten Congress Bells in the Old Post Office clock tower?

ANSWERS

708. Robert Byrd (D-W.Va.).

709. He leased an apartment in 1941 because his daughter's schooling was being split between Washington and Missouri, and it was wartime, when Congress was expected to be in uninterrupted session.

710. At lawyers' desks in the Old Supreme Court Chamber.

711. Over two miles—12,000 ft.

712. A committee set up for a limited time and purpose.

713. The Copyright Act, 1870.

714. By the light of oil lamps and candles.

715. Yes.

716. 2,953 lbs.

717. During whose presidency was the view destroyed between the Capitol and the White House?

718. A House resolution in 1965 approved $750 for every Congressman to hire these young people for the summer.

719. Were Capitol security officials able to detect the unauthorized presence of chemical and biological substances before 11 September 2001?

720. George Munger's 1814 watercolor of the burned-out Capitol is in this Washington, D.C. art collection.

721. Why did Sen. Thomas Gore (D-Ok.) squeeze a folded, written prophesy into a crack in his Senate desk in 1921?

722. Why did Rep. Usher Burdick (R-N.D.) rise in July 1951 to wish his House colleagues "Merry Christmas and a Happy New Year."?

723. Where did the Senate hold hearings into the sinking of the *Titanic* in 1912?

ANSWERS

717. Under Andrew Jackson, when the Treasury building went up and obscured the view.

718. College student interns.

719. Yes.

720. The Kiplinger Washington Collection.

721. As forecast after his defeat, he was re-elected a decade later and retrieved the note to boast of his prophesy.

722. He spoke so rarely that he took the opportunity to wish everyone season's greetings after giving a short speech.

723. In the exquisitely decorated Caucus Room of the Russell Senate Office Building.

724. How many votes did the framers of the Constitution require of the House and Senate before each could expel one of its members?

725. How many hallways of vivid paintings make up the Brumidi Corridors?

726. When is the Senate charged with electing a vice president?

727. Which House and Senate officials arrange funerals for members who die in office?

728. How many rooms had the Senate convened in before moving into its current chamber?

729. What did the Hall of the House of Representatives double as in the early 19th century?

730. Guess which year the large crystal chandelier in the Senate Appropriations Committee room was acquired from the White House.

ANSWERS

724. Article I section 5 required each house to have two-thirds voting for expulsion.

725. Five—the main, west, inner, north, and Patent corridors.

726. When none of the candidates has a majority of electoral votes, the Senate chooses between those two with the highest number.

727. The House and Senate sergeant at arms.

728. Two.

729. A venue for church services and public meetings.

730. 1903.

731. How did architect Benjamin Henry Latrobe describe the building he had just finished to house Congress while the Capitol burned by the British was being rebuilt?

732. When did Congress begin publishing its proceedings under its own direction?

733. This Senate President would have succeeded to the presidency if Abraham Lincoln had been assassinated six weeks earlier.

734. Why did House Democrats sing *Home, Sweet Home* with such gusto in 1891?

735. How many people could the galleries accommodate when the new Senate chamber opened in 1859?

736. What is a Pocket Veto?

737. Kentucky first elected this Hall of Fame baseball pitcher to the U.S. Senate in 1998.

738. At what Washington, D.C. address did the foremost painter of the Capitol, Constantino Brumidi, die on 19 February 1880?

ANSWERS

731. "An admirable substitute for the Capitol."

732. 1873 in the *Congressional Record.*

733. Hannibal Hamlin, who was vice president until Andrew Johnson was sworn in as Lincoln's new vice president just six weeks before the assassination.

734. So many laws had been passed in that busy 51st Congress that it was a spontaneous reaction when the Speaker gaveled it to a close.

735. One thousand.

736. If the president fails to sign Congressionally approved legislation within 10 days, during which Congress adjourns, the legislation dies.

737. Republican Jim Bunning.

738. 921 G Street NW.

739. Who is responsible for Capitol accessibility for the blind and deaf, and those in wheelchairs?

740. Some Library of Congress books used to be shelved in the visitors' gallery of this former debating hall.

741. This President of the Senate died in 1899 before his term of vice president expired.

742. How much did Congress appropriate to cover the cost of the Lewis and Clarke Expedition?

743. Which president came in for withering Congressional criticism for furnishing the White House like "a palace as splendid as that of the Caesars."?

744. Which State donated the statue of Andrew Jackson in the Rotunda?

745. Which president gave final approval for construction of the dome?

ANSWERS

739. Congressional Special Services Office.

740. The Hall of the House of Representatives, now Statuary Hall.

741. Garret Augustus Hobart, Republican.

742. More than $38,000.

743. Martin Van Buren in 1840.

744. Tennessee.

745. Franklin Pierce in 1855.